When Grandma was Young

Paul Humphrey

Illustrated by
Katy Sleight

Evans

Yippee! It's Grandma!

4

5

Are you very old Grandma?

6

Yes. But I was young once.

7

When I was young people
wore clothes like this.

9

10

When I was young the streets looked like this.

When I was young cars
looked like this.

When I was young trains looked like this.

What were toys like when you were young Grandma?

16

When I was young toys were
like this.

When I was young I listened to the wireless.

When I was young I went
dancing.

21

When I was young I rode my bicycle.

23

When I was young I went to
the beach.

*Really
Grandma?*

25

You had fun when you were young Grandma.

Yes, I did.

28

29

Some of the things on this page belong to Grandma's time and some belong to today. Which ones are which?